CW00703911

FIGHTING LOW SEX DRIVE IN WOMEN: *Addressing some of the non-medical causes and solutions for low sex drive in women.*

By

Lucille Brown

FIGHTING LOW SEX DRIVE IN WOMEN:
Addressing some of the non-medical causes and solutions for low sex drive in women.

By

Lucille Brown

All rights reserved © 2018 by Lucille Brown

No part of this book may be reproduced or transmitted in any form or by any means, graphic, electronic, or mechanical, including photocopying, recording, taping, or by any information storage retrieval system, without the written permission of the publisher.

FIGHTING LOW SEX DRIVE IN WOMEN: *Addressing some of the non-medical causes and solutions for low sex drive in women.*

This book is not being written as a medical guide and should not be taken as one. It is a book based on conversations with women who have experienced the problem of a low sex drive. How did they increase their sex drive? Did they have to make any changes to their lives? And if they did, were those changes easy or painful? Did any of them have to change their way of thinking about certain things? Each of the women's stories have been transformed into a letter format to fit the style of this book.

Many marriages are suffering because one member has a low sex drive which causes the other partner to feel rejected or unloved and dissatisfied with the physical intimacy. We can no longer be passive and watch our relationships wilt away!

It is time to explore some of the causes and solutions to the problem of a low sex drive, and time to learn from the journeys of other women, in order to find the solution that works best for each of us, to help us have a happier and healthier sex life.

Some of the causes of a low sex drive are the following:

1. Medical reasons
2. Depression
3. Stress
4. Relationship issues
5. Self-esteem
6. Lifestyle habits
7. Exhaustion
8. Eye Gates and Ear Gates

MEDICAL REASONS

As mentioned already, this book is not medical in nature so I shall say only a few words under this topic in order to let you know that a low sex drive can be caused by both medical and non-medical reasons.

Various diseases and prescriptions are known to cause low sex drive so if you only began to experience low sex drive after being diagnosed with a particular illness, or after beginning a particular prescription, you can discuss this with your doctor. Also, hormonal changes that occur in a woman's body during Menopause, Pregnancy and Breastfeeding may affect some women's sexual desire.

DEPRESSION

Depression, is a factor that can affect your sex drive. When you're in the pit of depression and everything looks gray and miserable, there is usually no desire to engage in sexual activity. The solution, when it comes to depression, is to find the source or the root of these feelings because there is almost always a reason why you are depressed, unless your depression is caused by a chemical imbalance in your brain or another medical reason.

If your depression is not being caused by a medical factor, then you must take time to be quiet and think honestly about what is causing you sorrow. You must be willing to be honest with yourself since the truth may not be pleasant to admit.

Julie's story:

A part of me always knew the reason for my constant depression even though I didn't want to admit it to myself, but one day when my husband came home and said to me "Julie, I just can't take this anymore! You're always sad and I don't know what I've done wrong. I can't take this anymore..." I knew I had to deal with this. I went into our Entertainment room and curled up on the sofa with a book, pretending to read. I thought long and hard and I finally admitted to myself that the reason I was constantly depressed was because of my first boyfriend. We had dated from when we were 16 to about 19 and I really thought we would get married. But he met someone else in college. Even though I later fell in love with someone else too and got married, a part of me had never let go of my first boyfriend.

Having come face to face with the truth, I had to make a choice. Was I going to continue thinking about my first boyfriend, always wondering if we had make a mistake? Or was I going to accept that the great guy I had married was meant for me? After talking with you, I realized that I had fallen into "the grass looks greener on the other side" trap, where other people's lives look perfect because you don't see all that's going on with them and you begin to feel as if your life is not so great! I came to a decision. My husband was a great guy who loved me and honestly I really did and do love him, and I did not want to lose him due to a stupid pining for an old love which may have never even turned into a great marriage! After this change/firm decision in my mind, my whole thinking and emotions began to change. I began to feel lighter and with time happier, and yes this has translated to me wanting my husband to touch me. I finally have a sex drive, lol!

STRESS

Stress is another factor that can affect your sex drive and it works in a similar way to depression even though it can make you very irritable unlike depression which usually leaves you listless and passive.

When you're dealing with financial stress or stress from problems at work or home, it is difficult for your brain to get relaxed enough to feel any desire for your partner. If the stress is something that can be alleviated without causing you trouble then it may be best to take that route. For instance if you're in a stressful work environment and you know you have a lot of savings and good working credentials to find another job without using too much of your savings, then you may need to leave that workplace. If on the other hand you are financially dependent on the job, you may have to find other means of alleviating the stress, such as exercising, massages, or talking to your spouse or other family member or a counselor about problems at work, since it is very therapeutic to let out your frustrations verbally.

However, please remember that if you are telling someone about your work problems every day, your kind listener will eventually become weary and frustrated even though they love you, because no-one enjoys hearing negative news constantly.

It would be wise to talk to a counselor if you need to talk for more hours than your loved ones can handle!

Lydia's story:

My workplace was hell! The boss was actually really nice which might seem strange since most people with workplace horror stories always point the finger at the boss. But in my case the boss was great, it was my co-workers who were incredibly difficult to work with. They were constantly insulting other workers behind their back and when I started distancing myself from that toxic environment and stopped hanging out in the breakroom with them, they made me their new target. They became unfriendly toward me and were constantly gossiping about me- I could tell because of how conversations would stop abruptly when I was walking past them. I was miserable every time I returned home and regaled my husband with complaints! He was a great listener and he told me to either ignore them or talk to my boss about what was going on. I just didn't feel like I had enough proof to go to my boss so I just put up with the crap and vented to my husband every evening. Then one particular evening, when I started telling my husband what had happened at work that day, he snapped at me saying "I really can't handle anything about your work today, I've just had the worst day ever at my work and I honestly need to just watch some football now, I'm so pissed...".

I was pretty offended with his reaction at first and just stalked off, but after I had had some time to think I realized just how selfish I had been. I had been unloading on him all *these months never once thinking he might appreciate one week without me talking about my problems at work! Plus, when he said he had had the worst day ever at his work, I didn't even ask him about it and give him a chance to vent when he had been doing the same thing for me! I went back to apologize and we ended up having a great conversation, about both of our days. We also came to the conclusion that my situation at work could not continue, so I talked to my boss the very next day to find out if I could be transferred to a different department where I knew there was an available lateral move position. I was able to make that move and believe me it made a HUGE difference to my husband and I's physical relationship since I wasn't stressed and needing to vent every evening, but could instead enjoy a relaxing conversation with my husband and be emotionally and mentally ready for physical intimacy with him.*

RELATIONSHIP ISSUES

For most men, an emotional connection is not crucial to their enjoyment or desire for sex. However, this is not the case for most women. Women generally need to feel connected to someone in order to have any desire to be touched by that person. Therefore, if there are problems in the relationship, this may be the cause of your low sex drive.

Frequent Conflict: it is natural for every relationship to have a little conflict since you are two people with different personalities and backgrounds trying to live together in one space! However, if the conflicts are unresolved or too frequent, thus causing bitter silence and tense feelings in each other's presence then a woman's sex drive will be low.

Betrayal of trust: If your spouse has cheated on you, it may take time to be able to forgive him and not see the other woman's face in your mind's eye every time your spouse tries to touch you. However, if you have chosen to remain with him then you must make a conscious decision to let go of the anger and unforgiveness in order to have a happy healthy sex life again!

Poor communication of your sexual needs to your partner: Sometimes women want their partners to guess everything when it comes to giving them physical pleasure, but that doesn't always work out. Take the initiative to let your husband know which areas you enjoy being touched at or which positions your prefer more or which positions are painful for you etc.. And in order to be fair to your husband, find out which things he enjoys or does not enjoy for you to do for him as well. Do not take offense if he admits that he doesn't like it when you touch him a particular way! Understand that having this kind of communication may be the key to making the sexual experience more enjoyable than it has ever been for both you and your partner.

SELF ESTEEM

There is also the issue of how you see (or esteem) yourself. Do you have a low esteem of yourself? Maybe you think you're not a good catch for your partner? Or you think you are ugly? If you think those kinds of negative thoughts about yourself it can lead to a low sex drive because you will be constantly thinking that your spouse can't possibly be satisfied with you or that you are not even worthy of his touch. If you are overweight (and do not have a medical reason that prevents you from losing weight) then you can certainly begin dieting and exercising to bring your body/image to a place that you desire. Or, if you have an unflattering hair-style which can be fixed by a visit to the hairdresser, then by all means take care of that problem as well.

However, if the things that you are unhappy with, are things beyond your ability to change, such as you want to be as tall as someone else or have the shape of someone else's nose, then you have got to let go of those thoughts!

Please understand that everyone is beautiful in their own way, so it's time for you to accept your appearance and not feel ugly just because you don't look like some famous actor on TV. When you are satisfied with the way that you look, it makes you look confident and more attractive to others because you exude a sense of contentment with who you are.

LIFESTYLE HABITS

Our bodies are all different and as a result not all women will react the exact same way to intake of alcohol. For some women some wine or other alcoholic beverage can be perfect for creating a relaxing amorous feeling and thus increasing their sex drive, but too much alcohol can also lower their sex drive or put them to sleep!

Scheduling a night or two for physical relations might sound like an odd idea but it does wonders for a relationship, so long as both partners are in agreement. It allows you to prepare mentally and allows your amorous emotions to build up just like a car engine warming up on a cold winter morning. People warm up/prepare in different ways- for some it may be by reading a romantic novel, watching a romantic movie, drinking some wine, or thinking romantically about your spouse.

Aline's story:

I enjoy the sexual experience with my husband when I have drank some wine and am feeling a little bit tipsy. Ever since I started doing that, about 2yrs ago, it has made me actually look forward to having sex, compared to before when I just wanted to be left alone! It's also been really helpful to me that we've picked specific days (Fridays and Sundays) for our special nights since this allows me to be prepared, i.e. purchase my wine ahead of time, begin daydreaming romantically about my husband or and watch a nice romantic movie before we go to bed. Those things really put my emotions and my brain in the right place for sexual intimacy!

These changes to my lifestyle have enriched my marriage in a big way- my husband is happy to know that I'm satisfied after we come together, and I'm delighted to be able to enjoy the experience, unlike previous times when the experience was not very fulfilling.

EXHAUSTION

Exhaustion is another factor that can affect your sex drive. Sometimes you may be going through a phase in your life where you have to care for younger children or aging parents and the exhaustion leaves you with absolutely no energy or desire for sexual intimacy. Or, you may be dealing with personal illness or recovering from surgery and your body is just unable to respond to your partner due to the fatigue that you are experiencing.

In these kinds of situations, if you have a patient and understanding spouse you can explain what you are going through to him and assure him that this is just for a season, and that your low sex drive has absolutely nothing to do with your feelings for him, since that is the fear that usually arises in the minds of people when their partners are exhibiting a low sex drive.

Bear in mind that it is not easy for even a loving and patient spouse to patiently wait for this kind of season to pass, since it can be very frustrating for him when his sexual needs are not being met for a long period. Be as thoughtful and proactive as you can be by finding occasions to rest and restore your strength so that you will be energized to desire intimacy with your spouse at least once in a while.

Rebecca's story:

So I have one 2yr old girl and two 4yr old twin boys, and I'm probably the most tired woman in the world haha! My older sister who lives in a different state was worried about how exhausted my voice always sounded on the phone and even more concerned when I confessed to her that I wasn't even able to meet my husband's physical needs anymore and it was causing a huge strain on our marriage!

She advised me to ask my husband to help with the kids when he gets home from work, but honestly it didn't feel right to me to do so, because I'm a Stay-at-home mom and I feel like the house and kids are my career! It just didn't feel fair to ask my husband to help with them after he had been out working all day. My sister reminded me that I had also been working all day, even if it was in the house, cooking and cleaning and running after 3 active children to keep them from killing themselves lol. She said she was sure my husband would be willing to give me a break from the kiddos a couple of hours each evening if it would mean he got his wife back!

She told me to make sure to begin the conversation by focusing on his need, not mine. So I told my husband that it was very important to me to be able to fulfil him sexually and that I had missed the wonderful feeling of desiring his touch. And then I explained to him that it was my constant exhaustion that was causing my low sex drive and that if he could take care of the kids for an hour or two in the evenings I would be able to rejuvenate and be ready for intimacy a couple of nights each week.

My husband agreed readily and our relationship has improved so much ever since! Right after dinner, he stays with the kiddos for about 2 hours while I get to soak in the bathtub or hide away in the basement and read a good novel. I literally feel like a new person...

EYE GATES AND EAR GATES

A woman must be very careful about what she allows into her space through her sight and her hearing since those are things that can affect how she feels.

The connection between a woman's feelings/emotions and her desire for sex is so huge that it is very important for her to track what she watches or hears! For instance, if you allow yourself to be constantly involved in negative conversations or constantly watching things that depress you on television, it acts as a dampener to your libido.

I am NOT saying that if your husband or anyone else needs to talk to you about their personal problems or global problems, you have to shut them out. What I am saying is that if such conversations are for hours and are on a daily basis, it can impact how you feel within, and therefore it is very important for you to become your own personal guard controlling what goes in through your Eye Gates and Ear Gates.

Fara's story:

I was such a political news junkie for many years, and I was always upset and short-tempered as a result of that! There was never any good news. It was all bad news, always. I wasn't even sure it either of the political parties made any sense anymore. I even became an Independent, but I still wasn't happy.

I finally took your advice to only listen to news over the weekend (to ensure that I wasn't oblivious to things going on in my country and in the world) and to totally ditch all the news channels Monday through Friday. I started watching fun relaxing shows in the evenings, after work. I felt happier, more relaxed, all the tension seeped away over just a couple of weeks.

I honestly had no idea how much this would change my life! My sex drive has gone up from 10% to 80%, lol. I really wish I had taken your advice to cut down how much news I was listening to on TV, much earlier!

THE END

If you enjoyed this book, kindly leave a review on Amazon to encourage others to read it- Thanks so much!
Email me at authorlucillebrown@gmail.com if you would like to be notified whenever I publish a new book, or if your Ladies Group or Couples group would like to book me for my Author visits/Marriage Seminars.
Sincerely,
Lucille

10607387R00016

Printed in Germany
by Amazon Distribution
GmbH, Leipzig